MASTER MIND
Brain Teasers

Master Mind invites you to challenge your wits with a stimulating series of riddles, puzzles and quizzes designed for hours of Brain Teasing fun. You can play Master Mind Brain Teasers by yourself or with friends. There are puzzles to suit every taste—a cornucopia of puzzles to spark any party, brighten any evening.

So put your imagination on alert and get ready to enter the stimulating world of MASTER MIND BRAIN TEASERS.

Have your tried Tempo's other great puzzle books?

MASTER MIND
Brain Teasers

by Joseph and Lenore Scott

tempo
books

GROSSET & DUNLAP
A FILMWAYS COMPANY
Publishers • New York

Master Mind Brain Teasers
Copyright © 1973, 1978 by Henry Joseph Scott & Lenore Scott
ISBN: 0-448-16079-X
Tempo Books is registered in the U.S. Patent Office
Published simultaneously in Canada
Printed in the United States of America

A "NON-INTRODUCTION"

If you like to skip introductions to books, here is your chance. This introduction is a "non-introduction" introduction. Or, since a double-negative is a positive, then you have already begun to read the book without loss of time. Therefore the introduction has magically disappeared, even as you are reading it.

We hope these pages delight, tantalize and amuse you. In them you will find a wide variety of puzzles, diversions, games and amusements to fit all moods. Among the contents you can relax and dabble as you desire. Or, you can pit yourself against yourself—to the fullest of your capabilities. The choice is yours to make, in the pursuit of enjoyment.

Have fun!

Joseph and Lenore Scott

HOW MANY BUSES

During the long summer daylight hours, a man takes a 7 A.M. bus from New York City, which is scheduled to arrive at 7 P.M. in Cleveland, Ohio.

This company also has service from Cleveland to New York. These buses leave every hour on the hour, 24-hours a day, between the two cities.

As the man relaxes in his seat up at the front of the bus, he can see his driver wave at every Cleveland-to-New York bus of the same company.

From the time the trip started at 7 A.M. until the bus arrived at 7 P.M., how many Cleveland to New York buses of the company did he see (assuming all buses were running on schedule).

Turn the page, to check your answer. . . .

ANSWER

The man would see 25 Cleveland to New York buses. As he was leaving New York at 7 A.M. he would see the bus which had just arrived, that had left Cleveland at 7 P.M. the night before.

As he arrived in Cleveland, he would see the 7 P.M. bus of the following day just leaving on its trip. Therefore he would see each bus enroute that had left from 7 P.M. until 6 P.M. the next day, being 24 hours or buses, plus the 25th bus which was just departing at 7 P.M.

ARTIST'S ERROR

The artist for a playing-card company was asked to draw a Seven of Clubs for a new deck of cards. Five times in a row the drawing submitted was rejected by the manager, who wrote a note: "Incorrect. Draw Again". Finally, on the sixth try, the artist got it right. Which one is the correct design?

For the answer, turn the page. . . .

ANSWER

The middle card in the top row is the correct rendition of the Seven of Clubs.

E-N-G-A-G-E-M-E-N-T

Using the letters in the word *engagement*, try to find all the words of four or more letters that you are able. No proper names allowed. Neither should you count minor variations that merely change the tense, person or part-of-speech because the word is used different ways, or has different meanings. There are 28 words, at least, hidden here. Be happy locating 23 or more.

For the 28 words, turn page. . . .

_____ _____ _____

_____ _____ _____

_____ _____ _____

_____ _____ _____

_____ _____ _____

_____ _____ _____

_____ _____ _____

_____ _____ _____

_____ _____ _____

_____ _____ _____

ANSWERS

In looking for words of four or more letters, as based on the word ENGAGEMENT, and following the rules given previously, compare these against your own list:

agent	gang	meat
amen	gannet	meet
anent	gate	menage
ante	gnat	mete
eaten	magnet	name
enema	mane	neat
engage	mange	tame
gage	mate	tang
game	meant	team
gamete		

THAT'S NAUTICAL!

You've just finished your Power Squadron courses in Seamanship and Navigation. You can read charts, estimate current speeds for any time of day at any location, amd make vector projections allowing for wind and boat speeds.

Now to get in some boating and recreation time. You anchor in a beautiful bay, then hang the ladder over the transom to go swimming. You notice it's high tide, and the water just reaches the third step down on the ladder.

You consult your official Table of Tides to find what the tide will be five hours later, when you want to pull up anchor. Where you've anchored, the tide will be 7½ feet lower. You measure your ladder, and find the steps are nine inches apart.

Using your newly gained knowledge from your boating courses, what step will be at or nearest to water level on your swimmers' ladder, at the end of five hours?

Turn the page for the answer. . . .

ANSWER

Still the third step down. The boat floats up and down with the tide, so the water remains constantly at Step Three. That is, unless you cast anchor in water so shallow that you'll be aground when the water gets to low tide. In that instance you better go back to the Power Squadron for the next course, and forget about counting steps on your ladder, in favor of more important decisions.

MONEY IN REAL ESTATE?

You always felt you had a good sense of house design, and decided to go into the building business instead of the work you are in.

You talk to a banker into financing you, and obtain credit from a number of suppliers. You build the houses, and then go to sell them.

In due course, you do make sales, of $39,600 for each house.

On the first house you make a ten-percent profit. That you like! But by the time the second is sold, a weakening in the housing market finds that despite the $39,600 received, you have a ten-percent loss.

Everything considered, after all figuring, are you money ahead, money behind, or did you manage to just break even?

Turn the page, for your financial status. . . .

15

ANSWER

You lost. The first house cost you $36,000. A ten-percent profit of $3,600 brought the selling price to $39,600. The second house cost you all of $44,000. A ten-percent loss of $4,400 brought the selling price down to $39,600. So regretfully, your real-estate venture put you $800 in the hole, not considering intangibles such as your time, efforts and hopes.

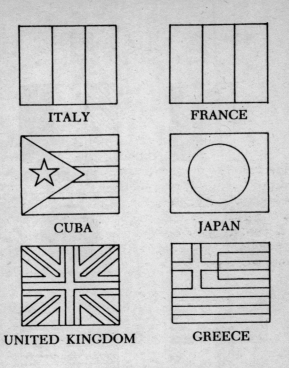

ITALY

FRANCE

CUBA

JAPAN

UNITED KINGDOM

GREECE

NAME THE COLORS

These six flags are well known. In each flag, write alongside, or upon the flag, the color shown on the nation's flag in each of the segments shown. Use abbreviations or initials for the colors, if you feel you haven't enough space.

Answers on the next page. . . .

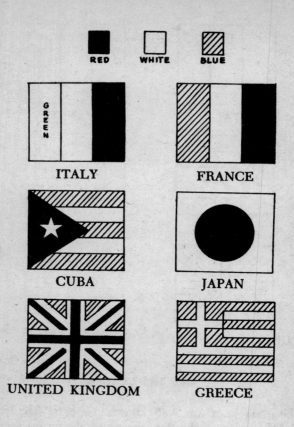

RED WHITE BLUE

ITALY

FRANCE

CUBA

JAPAN

UNITED KINGDOM

GREECE

ANSWERS

In these flags, the color code is shown here. Any other color is indicated upon the flag itself.

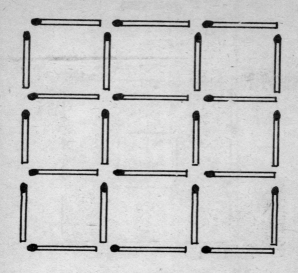

MAKE TWO BOXES

Lay out 24 matches, or toothpicks, as shown in the illustration here.

Now remove eight of the matches in such a way that you are left with only two squares. No shifting of matches, in this puzzle—just removing of eight.

Try for two different solutions, before looking at the answers.

Answers on the next page. . . .

ANSWERS

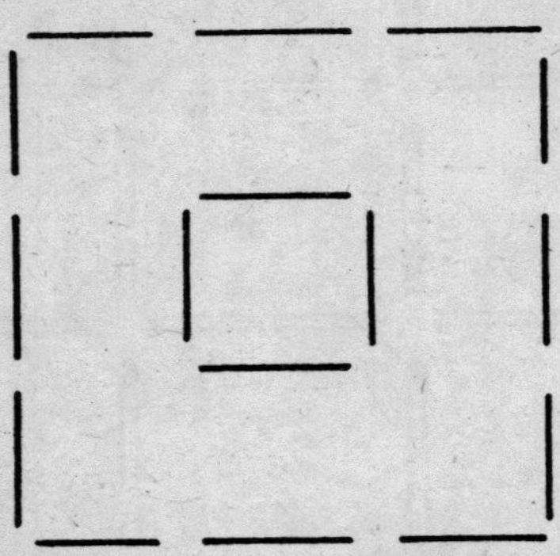

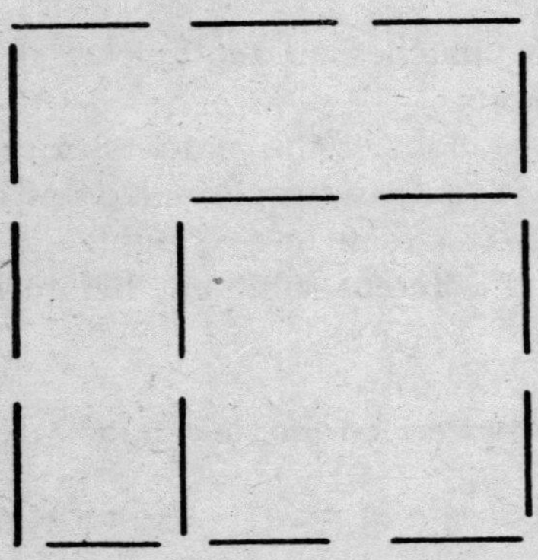

GUESS THE QUOTATION

Here are quotations from famous writers. The vowels have been left out, and spaces substituted instead. See if you can fill them in, each of which will take an A, E, I, O or U. Spaces between words are absent, so mark them with a slash "/".

1. TR__ST__V__RYB__DY,B__TC__TTH__
   C__RDS.
   —Finley P. Dunne

2. G__DH____LS,__NDTH__D__CT__R
   T__K__STH__F_____.
   —Benjamin Franklin

3. P_____PL__W__LLB__Y__NYTH__NG
   TH__T'S__N__T_____C__ST__M__R.
   —Sinclair Lewis

4. THR_____M__YK_____P__S__CR__T__F
   TW_____FTH__M__R__D_____D
   —Benjamin Franklin

5. M__RR_____G__H__SM__NYP_____NS,B__T
   C__L__B__C__H__SN__PL____S__R__S.
   —Samuel Johnson

6. TH_____NLYG__LD__NTH__NGW__M__N
   D__SL__K____SS__L__NC__
   —Mary Wilson Little

For the solutions, turn to the next page. . . .

ANSWERS

1. Trust everybody, but cut the cards.

2. God heals, and the doctor takes the fee.

3. People will buy anything that's one to a customer.

4. Three may keep a secret if two of them are dead.

5. Marriage has many pains, but celibacy has no pleasures.

6. The only golden thing that women dislike is silence.

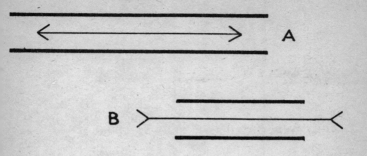

SEEING IS BELIEVING

Compare lines A and B in the first puzzle. Is A equal in length, longer, or shorter?

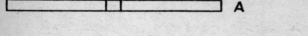

Some puzzles are easier than others, occasionally. The center-section of A, as compared to B, is the same size, narrower, or wider?

Answers are given on the next page. . . .

ANSWERS

The both lines in the first puzzle do look equal, don't they? They're not. A is longer.

In the bottom puzzle, it seems fairly clear that the central portion of B is wider. It isn't. Both central sections are the same size.

THE MAILMAN'S ROUTE

When the Post Office began making plans to deliver mail to the new housing development, the supervisor wanted a route as efficient as possible. Finally he developed one in which the postman would visit every home without crossing his own path during the entire trip. Can you do it?

Answer on the next page. . . .

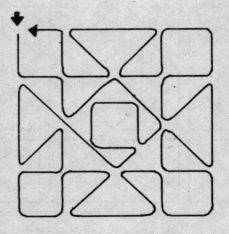

MUSICAL WORDS

If you look hard enough you can find the title of a well known opera in the sentences below.

Of the six operas, three are based on Shakespeare plays. The titles are hidden, as in "He *said a* lot by staying quiet." Somewhere in the line is the title of Verdi's famous opera, "Aida," as you can see by inspecting the letters. Now search for the six titles below.

1. He got hello and goodbye for all his troubles.

2. Poison sumac be the itcher, but butter be the soother.

3. Delilah am letting her hair down.

4. He changed the order of veal scaloppine into scampi.

5. Pueblo hen grind is a basic Mexican dish.

6. After being in limbo he met Satan.

For the answers, turn to the next page. . . .

ANSWERS

1. He gOT HELLO and goodbye for all his troubles.

2. Poison suMAC BE THe itcher, but butter be the soother.

3. DelilaH AM LETting her hair down.

4. He changed the order of veal scaloppine inTO SCAmpi.

5. PeubLO HEN GRINd is a basic Mexican dish.

6. After being in limBO HE MEt Satan.

TEN COINS NEEDED

With ten coins on the table in front of you, arrange them in a pattern so that you put them into five lines, each of the lines having four coins apiece. Imagination helps, in this puzzle.

Answer given on the next page. . . .

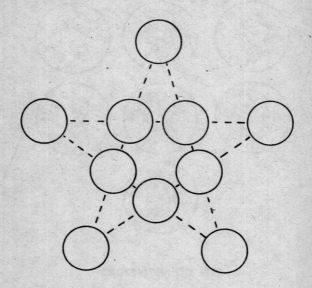

FOUR INTO FOUR

Trace these four pieces. You can use thin paper; trace through carbon paper onto thin cardboard; or press heavily with pencil onto blank paper underneath, then retrace. Cut apart. Form a 4-sided rectangle.

Solution is given on the following page. . . .

ANSWER

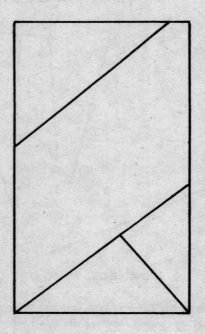

SQUARE-WORD PUZZLE

Here is a variation of a crossword puzzle. The task is to make a square of words so that the words read the same both across and down.

Clues to the words are in the following five lines. However, the sequence is mixed, so the answers might not come to you too easily.

1. To put on a chair
2. Heated bread
3. A strand of hair
4. Lubricator
5. One-celled plant, chiefly aquatic

For the solution, see the next page. . . .

ANSWER

T	O	A	S	T
O	I	L	E	R
A	L	G	A	E
S	E	A	T	S
T	R	E	S	S

HARD TIMES MADE EASIER

Things were tough for George. He had skidded down the economic ladder until he couldn't even afford cigarettes for himself anymore. So he started collecting cigarette butts wherever he could find them. He discovered that tobacco from six butts could be combined to form one cigarette.

He found 41 butts on one of his luckier days. Spacing out his smoking, he was able to begin a new cigarette every hour, commencing at 8 A.M. At what time did he start smoking his last cigarette?

Answer on next page. . . .

ANSWER

Eight hours later, at 3 P.M. When the first cigarette was smoked, made from six butts, he had a butt remaining. So his first cigarette consumed the tobacco of five butts, and left the contents of one butt which could be used in the second smoke. Continuing this way, he was able to make eight cigarettes, and still have one butt left for starting the next day's project of do-it-yourself cigarette making.

go ᴚ૪ש/o oʃʃɔɐᒪ8

"THE GOOD BOOK SAYS . . ."

For the following Sunday's sermon, the minister had printed in the church bulletin that it would be based on an important theme. The title would be shown in the cryptic writing reproduced above.

"Often," he said, "the messages you receive in your lifetime are not clear at first. Sometimes it takes great ability to read the signs. Other times you have to have the patience to give important ideas the time to develop."

What was the theme of Sunday's sermon?

For the answer, turn page. . . .

ANSWER

Hold the book up to a mirror, and read the reflection. The title for next Sunday's sermon was to be: "Do onto others".

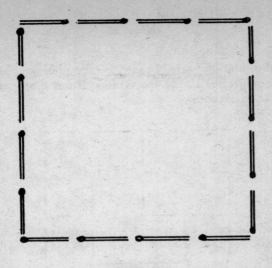

BOXED-IN

You have just rented the entire floor of a nice new office building. Great view from all sides! You have a problem in that four of the offices have to be the same size, or else you will have trouble with the four managers, who are jealous of each other. But being the boss, you want a third more space than they have.

Arrange the 13 partitions you have available, to divide the space as needed above. Each partition is proportionately equal to the length of one match, in the diagram shown here. That is the first problem.

Next, try it with 12 partitions. None are to be broken or bent. It is a harder problem, but it can be done. One office is for the photographic department, if that clue helps!

Answers are on the next page. . . .

In the solution with 12 matches, the photographic department prefers inside space, away from the windows, to set up darkrooms.

THREE SHORT PROBLEMS

The questions are short, but the solutions may not be as quick in arriving. Yet, try.

1. Write five numbers which are odd, rather than even, and have them add up to 14.

2. There are three children in the family: two boys and a girl. Their parents would like to increase the family so there would be twelve boys, and each boy would have a sister. How many more girls should they plan on?

3. What is the difference between six dozen dozen and a half a dozen dozen?

Answers on the next page. . . .

ANSWERS

1. 11
    1
    1
    1
   ———
    14

2. No more girls. The one girl they have would be a sister to any number of brothers.

3. Six dozen dozen is 864. Half a dozen dozen is 72. Therefore the difference is 792.

13-HOUR CLOCK

A harried businessman was so busy that his biggest wish was to have an extra hour a day. Being ingenious, he designed a face for his clock containing 13 hours instead of 12. But his assistant inadvertently painted the figures in the wrong direction.

Still ingenious, he then realized the possibilities for a puzzle to try at lunchtime. Do as he did: Draw the numbers 1 through 13 as shown. Then put numbered slips, 1 through 12 on top of the numbers, so as to match them. Leave 13 vacant.

Try reversing the numbers so as to read in correct clockwise direction. Any piece can move sideways one space into the empty spot then existing, or it can jump one number to get into the empty place. Moves clockwise or counter-clockwise permitted. The numbers can be reversed in 44 moves. Try it.

For the solution, see the next page. . . .

ANSWER

Move the numbers as mentioned. They will be in the correct position so as to be next to the empty space, or can jump one piece into the empty spot:

1, 12, 10, 11, 1, 2, 12, 10, 11, 8, 6, 4, 3, 5, 7, 9, 8, 6, 4, 3, 5, 7, 9, 8, 6, 4, 3, 5, 7, 9, 8, 6, 4, 3, 5, 7, 9, 10, 11, 1, 2, 11, 12, 11.

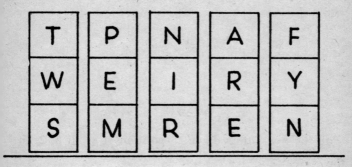

T	P	N	A	F
W	E	I	R	Y
S	M	R	E	N

1._____

2._____

3._____

DE-CODE THIS

One method of secret code writing involves moving strips of paper containing various letters. When put alongside each other in a certain sequence, they spell out a word or message.

Move these slips of paper mentally to see how quickly you can find the five-letter word contained in them. No switching of column positions or letters necessary. In your mind, pull each strip down to line 1, 2 or 3. Done correctly, you will find the word.

Turn page, if you get stuck. . . .

ANSWER

Pull the five letters down to positions 1, 3, 1, 3, 2, in that order. The answer will be SPRAY.

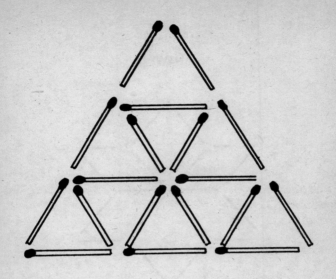

CHANGE THE TRIANGLES

Make a triangle out of 18 matchsticks or toothpicks as shown in the illustration. The object is to move six of the pieces, only, and make six new figures which have four sides apiece. These sides are not necessarily square. Mathematically, you could call them quadrilaterals. There are two solutions to this problem, if you care to seek them.

Turn page for answers. . . .

AN UNUSUAL STAR

There are stars to wish upon, stars that guide navigators, and stars used by astrologers in casting horoscopes, stars for lovers, stars for camping under, and stars for making you feel serene.

Here is a different kind of star. It is made up of triangles. The more you look, the more triangles you will see. How many triangles are there, in all? Try counting them. There are more than you think.

Turn page for the answer. . . .

ANSWER

Count carefully and you will find there are 110 triangles in the star.

CHANGE OF CLOTHES

You're wearing a pair of stockings and get a run, or hole, on the right side of your right ankle. To overcome the problem, you use your ingenuity. First you turn the stocking inside out. Then you switch your right and left stockings. Now where is the hole?

To top everything, while you're leaning over to change your stockings, you brush the outer side of your right arm, just below the shoulder, against a freshly painted table. And you're wearing your new slipover sweater! To hide the spot, you turn the sweater inside out, and put it on front to back. Fortunately the sweater's design permits such a change. But just for curiosity, where is the paint spot now, on your sweater?

Turn page, for the answers. . . .

ANSWERS

With your stockings, you are no better off. The hole is now on the outer side of your left ankle, so it is just as visible as before.

The paint spot on your sweater is on the inside of the sleeve now on your right arm. If you had not switched front to back, the paint would have been inside the sleeve on your left arm.

ABBREVIATIONS: A TO B

In Webster's unabridged dictionary are many abbreviations. Here are a few in the a's and b's. See if you can identify them. For Latin words, give both Latin and the English equivalent, if you can.

Answers are on the following page. . . .

A.A.U.W. ———————— bf ————————
abp ———————— bg ————————
abs ———————— B.L. ————————
ad lib ———————— B/L ————————
admx ———————— bl ————————
afft ———————— B.L.E. ——— ————
anc ———————— B.M.E. ————————
a/o ———————— Bnss ————————
barr ———————— bp ————————
Bart ———————— B.P.O.E. ————————
B.D. ———————— bt ————————
bet ———————— B.V. ————————

ANSWERS

A.A.U.W: American Association of University Women
abp: archbishop
abs: absolute (sometimes "abstract")
ad lib: ad libitum (freely)
admx: administratrix
afft: affidavit
anc: ancient
a/o: account of
barr: barrister
Bart: Baronet
B.D.: Bachelor of Divinity
bet: between
bf: bold face
bg: bag
B.L.: Bachelor of Law
B/L: Bill of Lading
bl: bale, barrel, black
B.L.E.: Brotherhood of Locomotive Engineers
B.M.E.: Bachelor of Mining Engineering
Bnss: Baroness
bp: birthplace, bishop
B.P.O.E.: Benevolent and Protective Order of Elks
bt: bought
B.V.: Beata Virgo (Blessed Virgin)

EIGHT TRIANGLES POSSIBLE

These two lines are the same length. See if you can add four more lines to this drawing. All the new lines must be the same length as the original lines shown.

If done correctly, you can have eight equilateral triangles. That is, each side of any triangle will be the same length as either of the other two sides of the triangle.

Solution shown on the next page. . . .

ANSWER

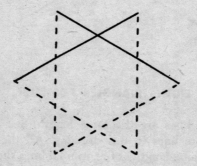

SO SORRY

The teacher was giving a lesson to the students in how to make change with different coins, to teach them both counting and the inter-relationships of various kinds of money.

George had $1.15. But each time he was asked to make change he said "Sorry, I can't do it." After hearing this statement several times, the teacher became annoyed and went to look at his box of money. Surprisingly, he was right.

—He had no dollars (paper or silver)
—He could not change a one-half dollar coin
—He couldn't make change for a 25¢ piece.
—Even for a dime, he could not make change.
—Neither did he have change for a nickel.

Therefore, what coins did George have, in order to possess $1.15?

For the answer, see the next page. . . .

ANSWER

George's collection of money consisted of four dimes, a quarter, and a half-dollar coin.

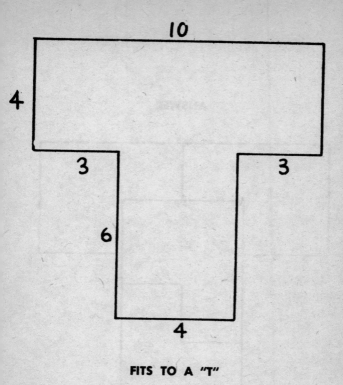

FITS TO A "T"

Draw a T that is the same size as shown. Trace it, or draw on another sheet through carbon-paper tracing. Or, follow the dimensions shown.

Now see if you can cut the T into four pieces in such a way that each of the pieces is the same shape and size as the others. Practicing with a pencil before making the cuts may be helpful.

Solution to the puzzle is on the next page. . . .

ANSWER

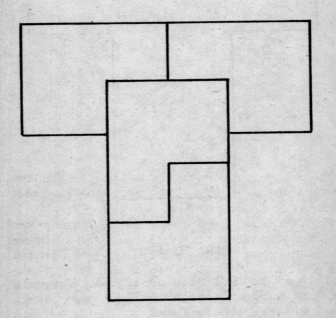

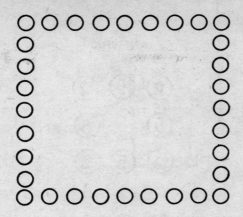

ALWAYS 9 PER SIDE

You can use 32 buttons all the same size for this puzzle. Or, with enough table space, a deck of cards or poker chips can be substituted.

From the original layout, rearrange the square so you still have nine pieces per side, yet are able to remove four of them from the game during the rearranging. You can pile buttons or cards on top of each other, if necessary. Any quantity in a pile still counts as part of the total being sought.

Ready for the second puzzle? Remove another four pieces, yet have the arrangement so there are still nine pieces on each side.

Want a third challenge? Remove four more pieces, still leaving nine pieces on each side.

Turn the page, for the three solutions. . . .

ANSWERS

② ⑤ ②

⑤   ⑤   28 pieces

② ⑤ ②

③ ③ ③

③   ③   24 pieces

③ ③ ③

④ ① ④

①   ①   20 pieces

④ ① ④

YOUR WORD POWER

Good with your vocabulary? Try these.

1. In Webster's unabridged dictionary is the following word. Care to guess what it means?

PNEUMONOULTRAMICROSCOPICSILICOVOLCA-
NOKONIOSIS

2. There is a fourteen-letter word which repeats the same vowel six times. Know what it is?

3. See if you can think of a word that has three double-letters, all next to each other. It is a common English word.

4. Try finding a word in the English language which has all the vowels in it: A, E, I, O, U.

Turn page for the answers. . . .

ANSWERS

1. The word describes a disease of the lungs caused by inhaling minute mineral or metal particles, which is called "pneumoconiosis", that occurs especially among miners when they inhale very fine dust containing silica or quartz.

2. Indivisibility.

3. Bookkeeper.

4. Questionable.

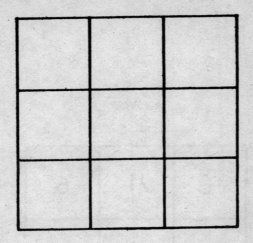

45 ALL WAYS

In this magic square, all rows lead to the number 45, when done correctly. This includes the sum of all horizontal rows, vertical rows, and the two main diagonals.

Use the numbers 3, 6, 9, 12, 15, 18, 21, 24, 27. Put one number in each box so that the sum of each row equals the "45" total.

There are several possible ways of doing it, but for one of the answers,

See solution on next page. . . .

18	21	6
3	15	27
24	9	12

EYE TEST

See how well your eyes can judge sizes and distances. In the first puzzle. is A longer, shorter, or equal in size to B?

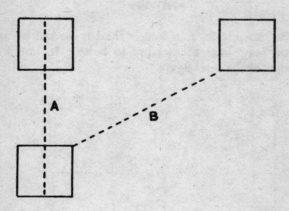

Test your eye-skills here too. Is A longer, shorter, or equal in size to B?

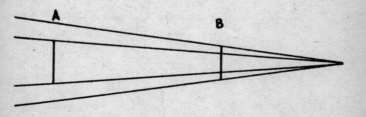

Answers to both tests are on the next page. . . .

ANSWERS

In the top puzzle, A is longer than B. In the bottom one, you may want to measure to believe it, but A is the longer of the lines again.

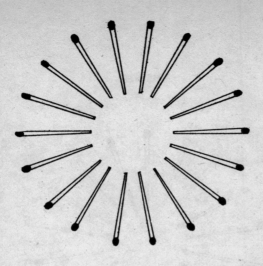

HEADS YOU'RE OUT

Arrange eighteen matches in a circle, all with their heads pointed out. Now turn certain ones in the other direction so that the heads point inward. If you select the correct matches to turn, you can do the following trick successfully:

Start anywhere with match Number 1, and count to the ninth match. Remove it. Then count nine more and remove the match. Keep going around the circle removing every ninth match. In due course you will have only nine matches left, all with the heads pointed in. All the matches removed will have had their heads pointing outwardly when taken.

Solution is on the next page. . . .

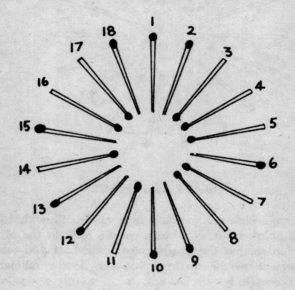

A MATTER OF RELATIVITY

Some people are hopeless in figuring out who is related to whom. You ask what the relationship is of their mother's brother to themselves, and they struggle ten minutes before saying "Uncle!"

But of course your adeptness is greater than that. So try your skill with these relationships:

1. What is the relationship of your mother's brother's brother-in-law to you?

2. The man referred to the lady whose son was the sole brother-in-law to his maternal grandfather's only boy. He was referring to:

3. In this instance the conversation was about a man's wife's brother's sister's mother's son-in-law's brother's wife's son's mother's mother. The conversation was about whom?

If you have in-law troubles here, turn the page for
the answers to your problems!

ANSWERS

1. Your father.

2. His paternal grandmother

3. The man's brother's mother-in-law.

WHAT'S THE QUOTATION?

Substitute the original letters for the ones shown, and you will have a famous quotation. Space is left under each word so you can enter your own letters.

FRGW DK YZMG UFGHCU IRHI

URG XU DHSG ZP ICAIR, X SZ

OGYXGMG RGC, IRZABR X LWZF

URG YXGU

FXYYXHD URHLGUVGHCG

For solution, see the next page. . . .

ANSWER

"WHEN MY LOVE SWEARS THAT SHE IS MADE
OF TRUTH, I DO BELIEVE HER, THOUGH I KNOW
SHE LIES"

WILLIAM SHAKESPEARE

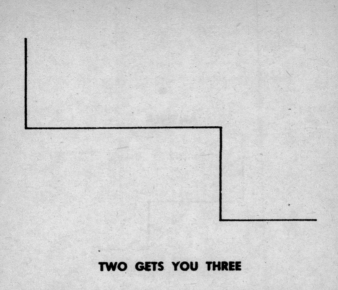

TWO GETS YOU THREE

By adding two straight lines to this illustration you can make three triangles, all the same size.

Solution on next page. . . .

ANSWER

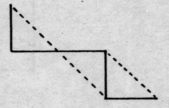

WHAT'S THAT SCORE?

The crowd is cheering. An official league game is in progress to settle the state championship. It is the top of the fifth inning, and the Sluggers lead their opponents 4 to 0. Yet despite following all the rules, and the Sluggers having a four-point lead, not a man has passed second base.

Truth is stranger than fiction, sometimes, in order to have this happen. Think of the rules you have learned regarding baseball. See if you can figure out how the Sluggers earned their score.

Solution on next page. . . .

ANSWER

The game is for state championship between two girls' teams.

ABCDEFGHIJKLMNOPQRSTUVWXYZ

Switch the A and the B in the headline above, and you will have a different way of combining the 26 letters of the English alphabet. Transfer the positions of the A and C, and you have another variation.

Suppose you wrote the various possible combinations of the alphabet on a long sheet or roll of paper. Normal typewriter spacing is six lines per inch or 72 lines per foot. Most computers have the same spacing. A mile's worth of lines would be 381,160 lines, if you find the information helpful.

Make a guess as to how long the sheet of paper would be, to contain all the possible variations of writing the 26 different letters of the alphabet.

Now turn page for the actual answer. . . .

ANSWER

If you want the solution in terms of *miles*, it is 1,060,846,646,482,020,000,000 miles long!

Put another way, if you want to get down to the basic information, there are approximately 403,291,-461,126,605,635,584,000,000 possible combinations.

Or taking another way to visualize the length of that sheet or roll of paper, it would go around the earth at the equator 42,664,282,991,240,000 times (or possible a whisker less, if you want to decide what thickness of paper you would type on, or run through the computer!)

E O V Y O F L I D E E L V B

U   O

A   A

W   L

N O D U B L E D L B O E V

By skipping letters in a pre-determined uniform sequence (you find that sequence), and moving around the pattern of letters from a specific point, you should be able to find an interesting quotation. A comma is purposely left out, to avoid making the puzzle too easy.

The answer is on the next page. . . .

ANSWER

Start with the letter I in the middle of the top row, and read every-other letter, going counter-clockwise. The quotation is "If you would be loved, love and be lovable."

12	6	22	26
10	32	20	2
18	14	28	8
4	30	24	16

AIM FOR HIGHEST SCORE

In the boxes shown are various numbers. Add the figures in the boxes which are crossed by the straight line, and you will get 112.

With some more observation, using one straight line, you should be able to reach a higher number.

What is the highest total you can find?

For the answer, see the next page. . . .

12	6	22	26
10	32	20	2
18	14	28	8
4	30	24	16

ANSWER

Adding the numbers shown in the boxes crossed by the solid line, a total of 150 can be reached.

ONE LINE/NO CROSSING

Each of the illustrations can be drawn with just one line, without removing your pencil from the paper, and without re-tracing any of the lines.

The more challenging problem is to draw them without moving your pencil over a line already made. Can you do it?

Answers on the next page. . . .

ANSWERS

On the illustration of the envelope, there are 50 different ways it can be done, without lifting your pencil from the paper, and without retracing a line. This includes some ways in which pencil lines might cross each other, and other ways where the lines do not cross another.

SAME AT BOTH ENDS

Here are some words in which you are supposed to meet yourself both coming and going. The first letters of each word are the same as the letters at the end of that word, and in the same sequence.

For instance, the obvious solutions to the word——PHA-BETIC——would be *ALPHABETICAL*.

After solving, or trying to solve these, you should find it challenging to discover other words on your own.

1. ___MA___
2. ___CI___
3. ___TI___
4. ___PERTOI___
5. ___STA___
6. ___RATEGI___
7. ___VE___
8. ___AS___

Turn page for answers to this puzzle. . . .

ANSWERS

1. TOMATO
2. DECIDE
3. RETIRE
4. REPERTOIRE
5. TESTATE
6. STRATEGIST
7. REVERE
8. ERASER

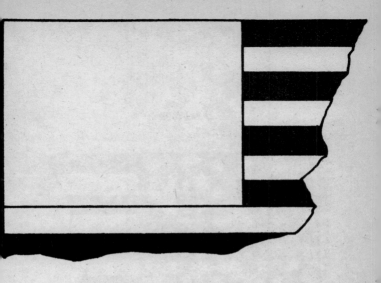

WHERE ARE THE STARS?

You have seen the United States flag often enough. Keeping its image in mind, see if you can draw the stars in the pattern as they appear on the flag.

Since the stars will take a lot of drawing, you might prefer to use substitutes, such as a small circle instead of a star, an asterisk (*), or perhaps a heavy dot (•).

Answer on the next page. . . .

DILUTING THE SCOTCH

The favorite hangout for the drinking crowd was filled, and the bartender needed five hands to keep up with the business. So when the newly arrived group of customers all asked for Scotch and water. he did the following:

Into a tall glass he poured ten ounces of Scotch. Into a similar glass he placed ten ounces of water. Then he poured one ounce of the water glass contents into a measuring glass and transferred the amount into the Scotch. After mixing the contents of the Scotch glass, he poured off one ounce and drained that small amount into the water glass.

"Now," he said, "see if you can tell me whether the Scotch in the water glass, when compared to the water in the Scotch glass, is more, less, or equal in volume."

Ten minutes later the group was still arguing and taking sides, so the bartender gained the time he needed. Actually, what is the right answer?

For the solution, turn to the next page. . . .

ANSWER

Actually, the amounts are equal.

Of the first step, one ounce of water moved to the Scotch glass left nine ounces of water in the water glass, and eleven ounces of contents in the Scotch glass: ten of Scotch and one of water.

On the second step, one ounce from the Scotch glass mixture consisted of one-eleventh of each liquid, so eleven ounces could be reduced to ten ounces. In decimals, 10:1 of one ounce is:

.9091 ounces were of Scotch

.0909 ounces were of water

Pouring this mixture into the water glass made ten ounces again, comprised of:

9.0000 ounces of original water

.9091 ounces of Scotch

.0909 ounces of water, back from Scotch glass

In the Scotch glass were ten ounces, made of:

Water: 1.000 ounces of water less .0909 removed, leaving .9091 ounces of water.

Scotch: Of the 10 original ounces, .9091 were removed, leaving 9.0909 ounces. So the Scotch glass has .9091 ounces of water, 9.0909 Scotch.

The amounts exchanged are equal. If the .0001 overage troubles you, use fractions instead. Though complex in figuring, equal answers evolve.

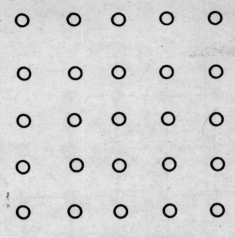

MAKE INTO 14 ROWS

There are twelve rows of circles in the illustration, if you count the rows containing five circles apiece. Five are horizontal, five vertical, and two are the main diagonals.

Now fill in 20 of those circles with a pencil. If you select the correct ones, you will have 14 rows, each row containing four solid circles.

Need help? The answer is on the next page. . . .

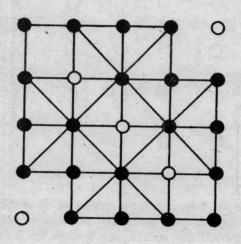

THE UN-CROSSWORD PUZZLE

This puzzle makes sense in one direction, but not in the other. So it is really an un-crossword puzzle. The correct words are to be placed vertically. Two of the letters are given that are found in each word. Clues to the words are not necessarily given in accordance with the sequence as required in completing the puzzle:

—To pardon
—A cutting tool
—Sweet citric fruits
—Shaking movements
—Associated with love
—Pursued academic studies in a lesser field

For the answers, turn the page. . . .

ANSWERS

1. Oranges
2. Forgive
3. Amorous
4. Minored
5. Tremors
6. Scissor

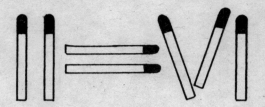

FOR A GENIUS FRIEND

Next time you are with a friend who thinks he is pretty good at math, try this one.

Place seven matches on the table, as shown here. They form an equation of "2 equals 6" (*VI*), which, of course, is not true.

Have your friend move only one match other than those in the "equals" pair. The match moved must end up making the equation true. In other words, the numbers on both sides of the "equals" mark have to be the same. No breaking or bending of matches is allowed. In fact,

try solving the problems yourself before turning page for the answer. . . .

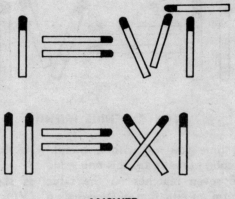

ANSWER

There are actually two solutions. The first is that 11 (in Arabic numbers) equals 11 (in Roman numerals). The other is that one equals the square root of one, as students of beginning algebra surely know.

Using the letters in the word THOROUGHLY, see how many words of four or more letters you can find. There are at least 33 words in common English usage here. Get 25 or more to do well. No proper names allowed. Neither should you count minor variations that merely change the tense, person, or part-of-speech because the word is used different ways, or has different meanings.

_____ _____ _____

_____ _____ _____

_____ _____ _____

_____ _____ _____

_____ _____ _____

_____ _____ _____

_____ _____ _____

_____ _____ _____

_____ _____ _____

_____ _____ _____

_____ _____

Turn page, for 33 words. . . .

ANSWERS

Searching the word THOROUGHLY for acceptable words of four letters or more, here are some possibilities you might check against your own list:

ghoul	hurl	rout	tour
glut	hurt	though	trough
gory	loot	thorough	troy
gout	lout	through	truly
grout	orgy	thug	tyro
holy	ought	tool	ugly
hoot	root	tory	your
hotly	roughly	tough	youth
hourly			

NUMBERS, PLEASE

Since you've seen enough telephone dials in your life to be thoroughly familiar with what they look like, test yourself. See if you can remember where the numbers and letters are located.

Write the numbers, and the correct group of letters, in the holes shown. Don't be amazed if you have trouble getting them right. Most people can not remember them successfully either.

For the answer, look at a telephone dial, or turn page for the correct solution. . . .

ANSWER

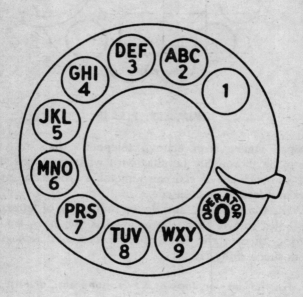

FIVE-WORDS SQUARE

Look at the clues below. Each of the numbers represents a line in the puzzle. The clue is the description or definition of a five-letter word that will fit into the boxes shown.

The first clue's words fit the first line, both across and down. The second line is for the second horizontal and vertical lines. The other three words follow in order. When finished, you should have a block of five words that reads the same both across and downwardly.

1. People who make fools of themselves.
2. To eat soup over-enthusiastically.
3. Coin of Ecuador; a capital of Bolivia.
4. A mistake, which isn't necessarily bad if used to advantage here.
5. Starts small, but in the end is whale-size.

Turn page for the solution. . . .

A	S	S	E	S
S	L	U	R	P
S	U	C	R	E
E	R	R	O	R
S	P	E	R	M

COIN-COUNTING

As he did each morning, the store cashier went to the bank to get $50.00 worth of change to put in his cash drawer. That would take care of any purchases made which required him to make change.

This time the bank teller was a new one. He gave $25.00 in $1 bills, $20 in $5 bills, and the remaining $5 in coins, consisting of 100 coins.

Upon getting back to the store, the cashier saw upon re-counting the money, that no 5-cent pieces had been included. How many of each type of coin did the bank give the store, to make up 100 coins without including any nickles?

Answer on the next page, if you want to look. . . .

ANSWER

One half-dollar coin, 39 ten-cent pieces, and 60 pennies.

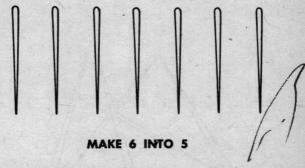

MAKE 6 INTO 5

Using six flat toothpicks, matches, or drinking straws, lay them out in such a pattern that they form five triangles. Don't bend or break any of them, in trying to do this puzzle . . . that is, unless you get frustrated and decide to break all of them anyway!

For the solution, turn page. . . .

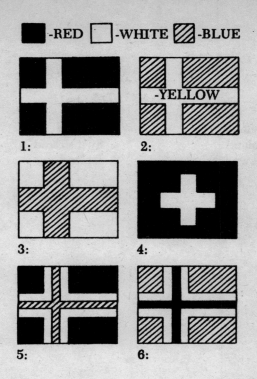

■ -RED □ -WHITE ▨ -BLUE

-YELLOW

1:
2:
3:
4:
5:
6:

NAME THE COUNTRIES

Name the country represented by each flag. Colors are as shown.

For answers, turn the page. . . .

ANSWERS

1. Denmark
2. Sweden
3. Finland
4. Switzerland
5. Norway
6. Iceland

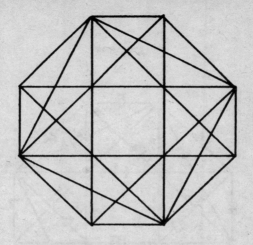

TRACE WITH ONE LINE

Here is a puzzle that will keep you going around in circles. Or, more precisely, going around in squares and octagons.

The object is to draw, or trace over, this diagram with one continuous line, without lifting your pencil from the paper. No tracing over a line twice, either.

There are numberous ways of solving this puzzle.

For one of the solutions, see the next page. . . .

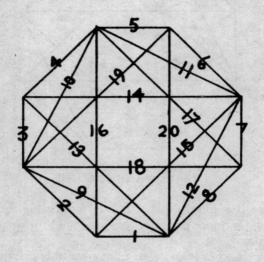

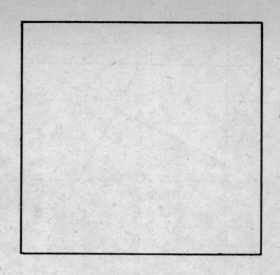

CUT INTO 5 SQUARES

Take a blank sheet of paper and cut into an exact square between five and ten inches per side.

The problem is to cut that square into smaller parts so that when they are fitted together you have five squares instead of one. All five squares will be the same size, with nothing left over.

This is not an especially easy puzzle to solve, so you may want to try laying out the lines on a scrap sheet of paper first.

For instructions and answer, turn the page. . . .

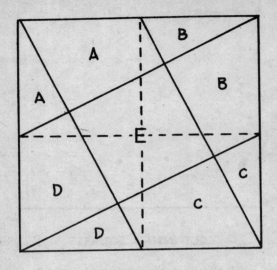

ANSWER

Fold or mark the original square of paper in quarters, as shown by the dotted line. Then rule and cut along the solid lines shown in the illustration. Notice that in drawing the lines, they meet either at the corners or middle of one of the sides of the paper. Match the pieces similarly numbered in such way that a square is formed, after cutting the paper apart.

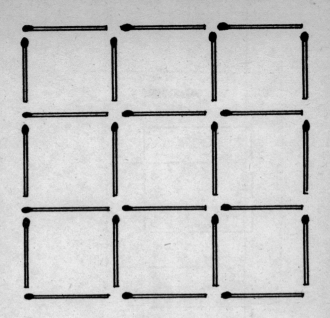

NOW IT GETS HARDER

You have probably tried matchstick problems before. Try this one, if you want a bit more challenge.

Lay out 24 matches or toothpicks as shown in the illustration. Now move eight of them in such a way that you form a total of only three squares. None of the pieces are removed, in this puzzle.

There are at least two ways of solving it. How many can you work out?

Turn page for the answers. . . .

ANSWERS

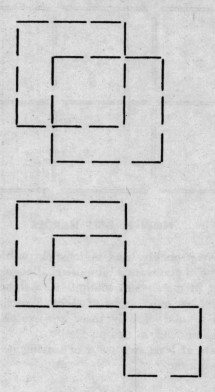

4						**4**	**2**
						4	
			1			**2**	
			1				
1			**3**	**2**	**4**		
			2				
1	**3**			**3**			
	3						

UN-SQUARES

Equip yourself with an eraser, when you try this one. You'll need it.

Note that there are four numbers, 1, 2, 3 and 4. Each appears four times. Draw a line along the lines only of the little squares, in any direction, so that all the Number 1's fit in the same section, without including any other numbers. Do the same for the 2's, 3's and 4's. The problem is to get each of those four shapes identical in appearance, yet containing only the four same numbers.

If you give up, see the next page for answer. . . .

ANSWER

4						4	2
						4	
			1			2	
			1				
1			3	2	4		
			2				
1	3			3			
	3						

1			
2			
3			
4			
5			
6			
7			
8			
9			
10			

WORD QUIZ

Below is a clue to each of the boxes. Clue numbers match row numbers. Just fill in the correct words. The words vary in length. However, the first letter goes in the left-side box; the last letter fits into the box at the right side. When done, you should have two additional recognizable words by reading the left and right vertical rows.

1—Royalty; ruler of a principality. 2—A religious leader. 3—Cause to feel self-conscious. 4—Consecutive. 5—Uncivilized. 6—Seductive, betraying woman. 7—Trade prohibition. 8—Confined. 9—A U.S. state. (Has at least one "T".) 10—Re the sun.

For the answers, turn the page. . . .

ANSWERS

1. Prince
2. Rabbi
3. Embarrass
4. Successive
5. Inhuman
6. Delilah
7. Embargo
8. Narrow
9. Tennessee
10. Solar

If you look down the first vertical row, and the last vertical row, you should find the words "Presidents" and "Eisenhower."

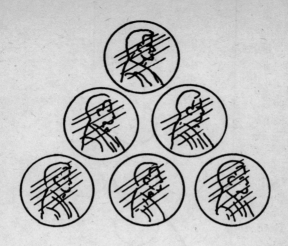

MAKE TWO ROWS

Take six coins—any denomination will do.

To make two rows of three coins apiece is easy, but can you make two rows of four coins each? That is a problem. If head-scratching and logic do not solve this for you in a few minutes, you may prefer taking a look at the answer. Two ways are possible.

For solution, see the next page. . . .

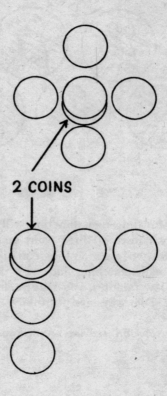

2 COINS

WHICH WAY IS UP?

You've earned a vacation, and it is a great one you have planned. Part of it includes an airplane tour around South America, with a side trip to the southern tip to see the famous and dangerous sea straits at Tierra del Fuego.

But when your airplane lands, you feel queazy. Maybe it is something you ate, or maybe psychologically you feel that being near the bottom of the world you are really upside down. So you decide to stand on your head, to get the sensation cleared away.

The time is noon, and the sun is to your right, while you balance yourself on your head. Which direction are you facing?

For solution, see the next page. . . .

ANSWER

You are facing east. Remember that south of the Equator the sun at noon is in the north. If you were standing upright, with the sun at your right, you would be facing west. Keeping that same side toward the sun, but turning yourself upside down, has you looking the other direction, or east.

Conversely, if you were north of the equator and stood on your head, with your right side toward the sun, you would be facing west. Do it upright, and you are looking eastward.

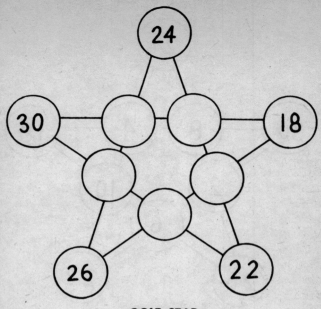

GOLF STAR

Look at your watch before starting this puzzle. The game is like golf . . . see how well you can do in getting into the right holes, with the lowest possible score.

In the five blank circles shown in the star, put the numbers 2, 4, 6, 8 and 10. They are to go in such a way that the total of four numbers along any of the straight lines in the star add up to 60.

For the answer, turn the page. . . .

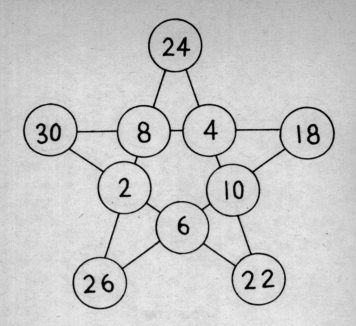

ANSWER

What was your score? The answer is shown above.
Try this on other people, and see how well they score.

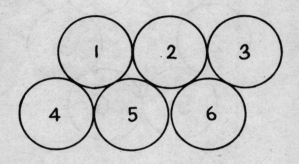

MAKE A CIRCLE

Here is a challenging puzzle to try out on friends. Put six coins on the table, laid out the way shown. The object is to move only one coin at a time, without disturbing others. In only three moves, change the two columns of coins into a ring of six coins. When a coin is moved it must touch two other coins.

For the answer, turn the page. . . .

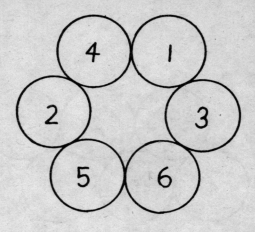

ANSWER

First, move 1 so it touches 2 and 3. Next, shift 2 so it touches top of 4 and 5. Finally, move 4 so that it touches 2 and 1.

CHANGE OF A DOLLAR

You're paying the check for your lunch at a restaurant in New York—a sandwich and coffee, which costs exactly one dollar.

You give the cashier 50 coins, instead of a dollar bill. All the 50 coins, when added up, come to just a dollar-even.

The cashier glares, but of course has to accept the money. The question is, in paying the dollar, how many of each kind of coin did you pay to the restaurant.

For the answer, if you need it, turn the page. . . .

ANSWER

Your payment consisted of:
$$25¢ - 1 \text{ quarter}$$
$$20¢ - 2 \text{ dimes}$$
$$10¢ - 2 \text{ nickels}$$
$$45¢ - 45 \text{ pennies}$$
$$\overline{\$1.00 - 50 \text{ coins}}$$

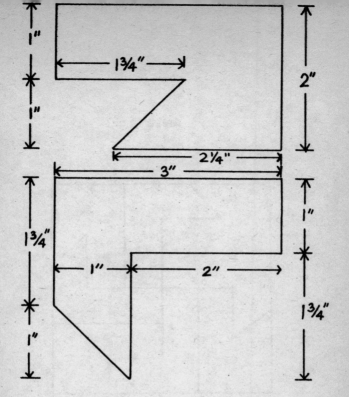

THIS IS CHALLENGING

Cut four copies of each of these two shapes out of a piece of cardboard. Trace the shapes shown. Or, draw your own pieces. The dimensions are given.

Now, form all eight pieces into one square. The sides shown here stay face up. In other words, solution of the puzzle does not depend on turning any pieces upside down.

Solution is given on the next page. . . .

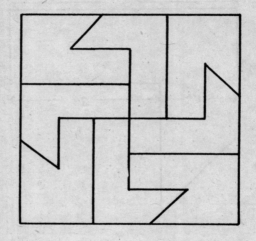

OH, SHAW!

In the lines below are quotations from the writings of George Bernard Shaw. See if you can work out the full quotation by discovering the missing letters. The dashes represent missing vowels: A, E, I, O, U. Space between words has been left out too, so put a slash (/) where spaces belong.

1. H_WH_C_N,D_ _S;H_WH_C_NN_T,
   T_ _CH_S.
2. S_CC_SSC_V_RS_M,_LT_T_D_ _F
   BL_ND_RS.
3. _SS_SS_N_T_ _N_STH_ _XTR_M_
   F_RM_FC_NS_RSH_P.
4. TH_G_LD_NR_L_ _STH_TTH_R_
   _R_N_G_LD_NR_L_.S.
5. L_CK_FM_N_Y_STH_R_ _T_F
   _LL_V_L
6. _P_RP_T_ _LH_L_D_Y_S_G_ _D
   D_F_N_T_ _N_FH_LL.
7. TH_R_ _SN_L_V_S_NC_R_RTH_N
   TH_L_V_ _FF_ _D.

For the solutions, turn the page. . . .

ANSWERS

1. He who can, does; he who cannot, teaches.
2. Success covers a multitude of blunders.
3. Assassination is the extreme form of censorship.
4. The golden rule is that there are no golden rules.
5. Lack of money is the root of all evil.
6. A perpetual holiday is a good definition of hell.
7. There is no love sincerer than the love of food.

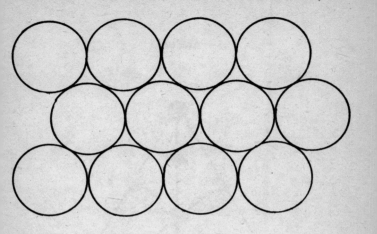

SEVEN ROWS OF FOUR

Here are twelve coins who want to get together. Can you help them?

They like it best when lined four in a row. Can you arrange them into seven rows, with still only four coins to a row?

If you find the solution becoming difficult, a pencil and paper may be helpful in testing out possible patterns.

To see how it can be done, turn the page. . . .

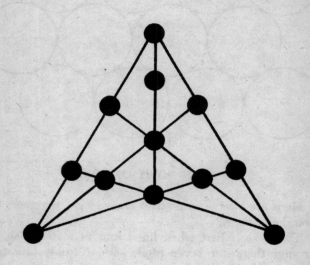

V–I–N–D–I–C–A–T–I–O–N

Try your skill again at finding words of four letters or longer, out of the characters shown in VINDICATION. No proper names allowed. Neither should you count minor variations that merely alter the tense, person, part-of-speech (verb into adverb, etc.), or identical spellings have different meaning. Of at least 36 words here in common English usage, see if you can locate 27.

_____   _____   _____

_____   _____   _____

_____   _____   _____

_____   _____   _____

_____   _____   _____

_____   _____   _____

_____   _____   _____

_____   _____   _____

_____   _____   _____

_____   _____   _____

_____   _____   _____

_____   _____   _____

Answers: turn page. . . .

ANSWERS

In the word VINDICATION, based on four or more letters being used, and other rules followed, here are some possible selections you might have made:

acid	canon	dint	iota
action	cant	diva	nation
adit	canto	divan	otic
anoint	canton	divination	tannic
anon	coat	icon	toad
antic	coin	indication	tonic
avid	contain	indict	vain
avoid	davit	into	viand
cannot	diction	iodic	void

SCORECARD

1	
2	
3	

SEE IF YOU CAN

Test your physical dexterity by trying to do the following:

1. Lie on the floor on your back. Cross your arms. Now get to a standing position without using your elbows or your hands.

2. Stand with your back to the wall. Drop an object near your feet, as a coin or handkerchief. Now try to pick it up, without bending your knees.

3. Lie on your back. Balance a coin on your nose. Without moving your head, try to get the coin off your nose by wiggling only your mouth and nose.

WHO IS GUILTY?

A loud bang of breaking glass awakened George from a sound sleep. He looked out the window, but nothing was astir up or down the street, nor among the houses across the street.

He looked at his watch, but it had stopped at 11:17. What a nuisance, since he depended on that watch in his busy schedule. A little winding on the stem started it again, so at least he didn't have to get it repaired. So knowing he had a busy day ahead, he crawled back into bed and fell asleep.

The next day the police stopped by, just as he was leaving the house. George didn't know what time it was, but it was early enough to yawn, ask what he could do for them, and also ask the time so that he could re-set his watch. It was now 7:30 A.M.

The patrolmen said they had picked up two strangers for suspicion, since they couldn't explain their presence in the neighborhood. Then they learned the house next door had been burglarized after a window was broken. One man picked up at 2 A.M. had a cut, which he said came from changing a tire. The other man was arrested at 4:15, and said he had tripped on a broken bottle while intoxicated. At least one man was innocent, the police felt, and perhaps George might be of help.

But George had not seen anyone. Besides, with his watch having stopped, he didn't know what time the robbery had occurred. However, he suggested that the police try a couple of the other neighbors. One was on a night-shift at the local electrical generating plant and might have seen someone; the other might have returned from vacation last evening.

Halfway to his car, George was suddenly struck with a flash of inspiration. He promptly turned around and went back to the policemen. It is not possible for the man arrested at 2 A.M. to be involved, he said, so at least he could be released from custody. How come he could reach that conclusion?

For the solution, turn to the next page. . . .

ANSWER

When George went back to bed, he wound up his watch. When the policemen stopped him it read 2:37. From the time his watch had started ticking again at 11:17, until 2:37, was a lapsed time of 3 hours and 20 minutes. Subtracting that much time from the policeman's time of 7:30 A.M. made it 4:10 A.M. when he had heard the glass break. So the man picked up at 2 A.M. could be safely eliminated as a suspect and released from jail, insofar as this robbery.

BIBLIOMANCY, BACKWARDS

An ancient method of predicting the future is to open the Bible to any page at random. Then, close your eyes and point your finger to any word at random. The word you hit is supposed to convey a message of significance to you.

Here's a way to reverse the procedure, and find someone's word without being told.

Have the person open the Bible (or any book) to any page. Write down the number of the page. Select any word in the first nine lines; then any word within the first nine words of that line.

Tell the individual to multiply the page number by 10. Then add 20. Next add the number of the line selected. Add another 5. Multiply by 10 again. Add the number which the selected word occupied in the line. The total is then to be told to you.

To yourself, subtract 250 from the figure you receive. The last number is the word position. The next to last figure is the line, and the remaining portion of the number is the page number.

PRESIDENT WHO?

Anyone who has taken a school examination about American history has felt the sensation this puzzle gives. The names get all mixed up, like the letters shown. History just refuses to make sense, at times!

In this puzzle are the names of all the Presidents of the United States. See if you can locate them. Only the last names are shown. Several men had the same name, so such names are shown twice.

Names are listed in a straight line. However, the lines may be horizontal, vertical, upward, downward, at a diagonal, backward or forward. Sometimes one or more of the same letters are used for more than one man.

Encircle the names you can locate. We'll start you off with the first Adams. Here is a list, since finding the names is hard enough, without asking you to remember the Presidents' names too!

Adams (J.)	Harrison, W.H.	Nixon
Adams (J.Q.)	Hayes	Pierce
Arthur	Hoover	Polk
Buchanan	Jackson	Roosevelt, F.D.
Cleveland	Jefferson	Roosevelt, T.
Coolidge	Johnson, A.	Taft
Eisenhower	Johnson, L.	Taylor
Fillmore	Kennedy	Truman
Garfield	Lincoln	Tyler
Grant	Madison	Van Buren
Harding	McKinley	Washington
Harrison, B.	Monroe	Wilson

```
    A B C D E F G H I J K L M N O P

 1  M O N R O E N H I C M T Y O T E
 2  A A X D J O H N S O N L P G A I
 3  D D R E L Y T G F O L E G A H S
 4  I A A R T H U R I L T V R R A E
 5  S M E M W A B A L I R E O F R N
 6  O S B H S R K N L D U S L I R H
 7  N I X O N D F T M G M O Y E I O
 8  H P J O R I V S O E A O A L S W
 9  A O U V A N B U R E N R T D O E
10  Y L L E E G V K E M G A E D N R
11  E K G R P I E R C E F U O N A C
12  S R O O S E V E L T N T F A P Q
13  N O T G N I H S A W N O S L I W
14  J O H N S O N H Y D E N N E K I
15  C H F I Y E L N I K C M S V C N
16  W J E F F E R S O N B R Y E L E
17  D J A C K S O N L O C N I L A D
18  H A R R I S O N N A N A H C U B
```

Turn page, to locate names you can't find. . . .

ANSWERS

The location of the first and second letters of each President's name is given after his name:

Adams, J.—2A, 3B
Adams, J.Q.—2B, 3B
Arthur—4C, 4D
Buchanan—18P, 18O
Cleveland—18N, 17N
Coolidge—1J, 2J
Eisenhower—1P, 2P
Fillmore—3I, 4I
Garfield—2N, 3N
Grant—3H, 4H
Harding—4F, 5F
Harrison, B.—3O, 4O
Harrison, W.—18A, 18B
Hayes—8A, 9A
Hoover, 6D, 7D
Jackson, 17B, 17C
Jefferson—16B, 16C
Johnson, A.—2E, 2F

Johnson, L.—14A, 14B
Kennedy—14O, 14N
Lincoln—17N, 17M
Madison—1A, 2A
McKinley—15L, 15K
Monroe—1A, 1B
Nixon—7A, 1B
Pierce—11E, 11F
Polk—8B, 9B
Roosevelt, F.—12B, 12C
Roosevelt, T.—9L, 8L
Taft—9M, 10L
Taylor—9M, 8M
Truman—4K, 5K
Tyler—3G, 3F
Van Buren—9D, 9E
Washington—13J, 13I
Wilson—13P, 13O

TAKE A MINUTE

Look at these cards for one minute, then put the book aside temporarily. See how many of the cards you are able to remember. Getting them all correctly named indicates near genius! Nine out of twelve is excellent.

THE GOSPEL TRUTH

Even though you start to have doubts while working with this puzzle, you are really dealing with answers that are for real—and that's the gospel truth! The scrambled letters on the opposite page are the names of the Books in the New Testament.

If you really get stuck and want some help, here are the names of the sections in the New Testament. These are in the order shown in the Bible. The scrambled words are in a different, mixed sequence:

Matthew, Mark, Luke, John, The Acts, Romans, 1 Corinthians, 2 Corinthians, Galatians, Ephesians, Philippians, Colossians, 1 Thessalonians, 2 Thessalonians, 1 Timothy, 2 Timothy, Titus, Philemon, Hebrews, James, 1 Peter, 2 Peter, 1 John, 2 John, 3 John, Jude, and Revelation.

1. HIP PIP NAILS
2. HOLE M NIP
3. REB WESH
4. MITY HOT 1
5. EUDJ
6. SASON COILS
7. T2REEP
8. INAS SHEEP
9. NOHJ
10. ITSTU
11. CHEATTS
12. AS MORN
13. JEE SAM
14. TINA HONES SALS 1
15. EPRET 1
16. WET THAM
17. TAG IN SALA
18. O 2TH MITY
19. NOHJ2
20. I NOR IS2 CHANT
21. KRAM
22. AS ON 2 NESTS HAIL
23. HONJ 1
24. TINA SIC HORN 1
25. HJNO 3
26. NOT VILE EAR
27. KUEL

Correct spellings given after the next page. . . .

1. _____	15. _____
2. _____	16. _____
3. _____	17. _____
4. _____	18. _____
5. _____	19. _____
6. _____	20. _____
7. _____	21. _____
8. _____	22. _____
9. _____	23. _____
10. _____	24. _____
11. _____	25. _____
12. _____	26. _____
13. _____	27. _____
t. _____	

ANSWERS

With correct unscrambling of the New Testament titles, this is the way your list should appear. The numbers coincide with the puzzle numbers. The sequence as the Books appear in the Bible are as given in the introduction section.

1. Philippians
2. Philemon
3. Hebrews
4. 1 Timothy
5. Jude
6. Colossians
7. 2 Peter
8. Ephesians
9. John
10. Titus
11. The Acts
12. Romans
13. James
14. 1 Thessalonians
15. 1 Peter
16. Matthew
17. Galatians
18. 2 Timothy
19. 2 John
20. 2 Corinthians
21. Mark
22. 2 Thessalonians
23. 1 John
24. 1 Corinthians
25. 3 John
26. Revelation
27. Luke

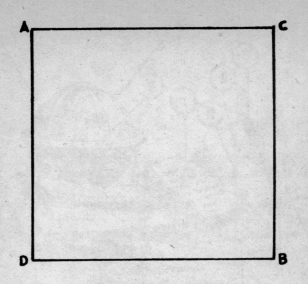

DONE WITH A MIRROR

This can be fun for yourself, and a good trick to try at a party.

Draw a square as shown here, on a piece of paper. Rest the paper on a book, magazine or table. Hold the paper in front of a mirror, or bring the mirror to the far edge of the paper. The paper is horizontal, and the mirror is vertical or upright, at a square angle.

Looking at the reflection of the illustration in the mirror, take your pencil. Draw diagonal lines within the box, from point A to B, and C to D. Be sure to look only in the mirror, and not at the paper itself.

If you can draw a straight line between the corners, you are quite unusual, because most people can not.

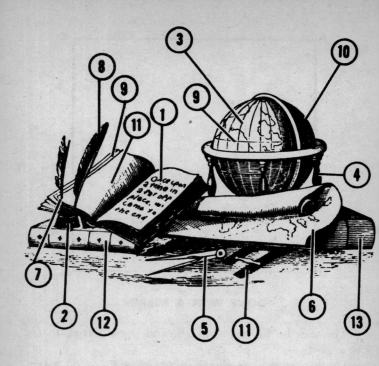

FOR ANCIENT MARINERS

Old map-makers and navigators had to use any information available to find their way around the globe. See how well you do identifying the items illustrated here, which were among the tools of their trade.

Fill in the correct words in the blank spaces on the opposite page. Numbers in the picture match numbers in the word-squares.

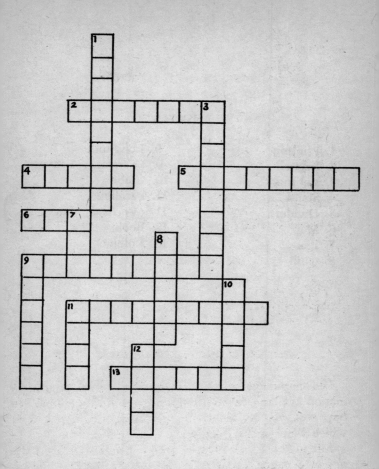

For the answers, turn the next page

ANSWERS

1. Printing
2. Inkwell
3. Latitude
4. Stand
5. Dividers
6. Map
7. Pen
8. Quill

9. Longitude
9. (*Vertical*) Leaves
10. Globe
11. Parallels
11. (*Vertical*) Page
12. Book
13. Volume

GUESSING GAME

Here is a procedure that will have your friends think you possess either ESP or mathematical skills.

Have someone toss a pair of dice so you do not see the numbers. Then ask the other person to look at one of the face-up numbers on dice. Either one will do. Have the individual secretly multiply the figure by 5. Then add 7 to the total. Next, multiply the answer by 2. Finally, add the number shown on the other die. Now ask what the total figure is.

In your own mind, deduce 14 from the total you have been told. The answer will give you two numbers. Those numbers will be the same as the original numbers thrown on the dice.

HEAVEN HELP YOU!

Try unscrambling the letters shown here. If done properly, you will have the names of the Books of the Old Testament.

You might desire a little assistance working with these names. Some of them are familiar; others are rarely heard. So here is a list of the Old Testament sections, if you want to refer to it.

Genesis, Exodus, Leviticus, Numbers, Deuteronomy, Joshua, Judges, Ruth, 1 Samuel, 2 Samuel, 1 Kings, 2 Kings, 1 Chronicles, 2 Chornicles, Ezra, Nehemiah, Esther, Job, Psalms, Proverbs, Ecclesiastes, Song of Solomon, Isaiah, Jeremiah, Lamentations, Ezekiel, Daniel, Hosea, Joel, Amos, Obadiah, Jonah, Micah, Nahum, Habakkuk, Zephaniah, Haggai, Zechariah, and Malachi.

1. BJO

2. GUS JED

3. AS HOE

4. NOT TAME SLAIN

5. AHA SII

6. AN HUM

7. TIC US VILE

8. I HEH NAME

9. KEEL ZIE

10. SEE SCATE LICS

11. AHA GIG

12. NOHJ

13. A HID BOA	26. DUE SOX
14. MONEY DO TRUE	27. HE REST
15. US LAME 1	28. FOG MOONS LOONS
16. SEE SING	29. SCONER CHIL 1
17. M. PASS L	30. RAZE
18. AH KAK KUB	31. I JAM HERE
19. SO A JUH	32. GINSK 2
20. ONJAH	33. AD LINE
21. HE HAIR ACZ	34. MEN RUBS
22. HEAH PANZA	35. THUR
23. HIM ALCA	36. SINKG 1
24. O SAM	37. ME US 2AL
25. AM ICH	38. BROVS REP
	39. SHINER LO2CC

**Answers to the scrambled letters are given on
the following page. . . .**

ANSWERS

If you are able to unscramble the names of the Books in the Old Testament, this is the list you should have. The number sequence follows the puzzle; the list in the introductory paragraphs gives the order in which they appear in the Bible.

1. Job
2. Judges
3. Hosea
4. Lamentations
5. Isaiah
6. Nahum
7. Leviticus
8. Nehemiah
9. Ezekiel
10. Ecclesiastes
11. Haggai
12. Joel
13. Obadiah
14. Deuteronomy
15. 1 Samuel
16. Genesis
17. Psalms
18 Habakkuk
19. Joshua
20. Jonah

21. Zechariah
22. Zephaniah
23. Malachi
24. Amos
25. Micah
26. Exodus
27. Esther
28. Song of Solomon
29. 1 Chronicles
30. Ezra
31. Jeremiah
32. 2 Kings
33. Daniel
34. Numbers
35. Ruth
36. 1 Kings
37. 2 Samuel
38. Proverbs
39. 2 Chronicles

HEAR! HEAR!

Take a long ruler or wooden dowel. Press one end tight against the flap covering the opening of your ear. (Don't put *in* your ear!) At the other end place a watch. You should be able to hear the ticking fairly well.

Other sounds to try might be slight scratching at the end of the stick. Or, if placed against a wall or floor, you can often know exactly what is going on or being said in the next room!

Someone hard-of-hearing with bone-conduction trouble can often hear music better than usual by placing one end of a ruler against a table or desk on which a table-model radio is playing, and pressing the other end of the rod against a tooth. Tone frequencies usually missed can be heard as the vibrations picked up through the tooth and bones bypass trouble in the ear's vibratory mechanism. A person with normal hearing usually can not notice any difference.

PICK A NUMBER

Ask anyone to select a number from 1 to 100, and keep it secret. However, have that person tell you in which Group the number appears. It could be in one or more of the seven Groups shown. You can quickly discover the correct number. Often this trick is done by asking the person to pick his age, or mentally decide any amount of pennies between 1 and 100.

The way of finding the answer is quite interesting, even if you have encountered this trick before.

For answer, turn next page. . . .

GROUP 1

1	21	41	61	81
3	23	43	63	83
5	25	45	65	85
7	27	47	67	87
9	29	49	69	89
11	31	51	71	91
13	33	53	73	93
15	35	55	75	95
17	37	57	77	97
19	39	59	79	99

GROUP 2

2	22	42	62	82
3	23	43	63	83
6	26	46	66	86
7	27	47	67	87
10	30	50	70	90
11	31	51	71	91
14	34	54	74	94
15	35	55	75	95
18	38	58	78	98
19	39	59	79	99

GROUP 3

4	22	44	62	79
5	23	45	63	84
6	28	46	68	85
7	29	47	69	86
12	30	52	70	87
13	31	53	71	92
14	36	54	76	93
15	37	55	77	94
20	38	60	78	95
21	39	61		100

GROUP 4

8	26	44	62	88
9	27	45	63	89
10	28	46	72	90
11	29	47	73	91
12	30	56	74	92
13	31	57	75	93
14	40	58	76	94
15	41	59	77	95
24	42	60	78	
25	43	61	79	

GROUP 5

16	26	52	62	88
17	27	53	63	89
18	28	54	80	90
19	29	55	81	91
20	30	56	82	92
21	31	57	83	93
22	48	58	84	94
23	49	59	85	95
24	50	60	86	
25	51	61	87	

GROUP 6

32	42	52	62
33	43	53	63
34	44	54	96
35	45	55	97
36	46	56	98
37	47	57	99
38	48	58	100
39	49	59	
40	50	60	
41	51	61	

GROUP 7

64	74	84	94
65	75	85	95
66	76	86	96
67	77	87	97
68	78	88	98
69	79	89	99
70	80	90	100
71	81	91	
72	82	92	
73	83	93	

ANSWER

Solution: Add the first number in the upper left corner of each Group selected. The total of such numbers will give you the correct secret number.

How come? If you are mathematically curious, these groups are based on Binary Numbers. If you know the binary system, any number can be expressed with a 1 or 0. For numbers 1 through 10, the equivalent binary numbers are: 1 is 1, 2 is 10, 3 is 11, 4 is 100, 5 is 101, 6 is 110, 7 is 111, 8 is 1000, 9 is 1001, 10 is 1010. 15 is 1111, 16 is 10,000. 32 is 100,000. 64 is 1,000,000. 99 is 1,100,011. 100 is 1,100,100.

Group 1 has any binary number where the last digit is a 1. Group 2 is any binary number where the second row from the right is a 1 rather than a 0. Group 3 contains binary numbers having a 1 in the third column from the right. Groups 4, 5, 6 and 7 require a 1 in columns 4, 5, 6 or 7 respectively, counting from the right.

So when Groups are selected, you are really being told which column has a binary indicator of "1." You could reverse the procedure, and request which Groups do not contain the secret number. Write a 7-digit binary number, with zeros in the Groups (Columns) being excluded. The binary number remaining gives the figure you seek. All you need know, now, is how to convert Binary numbers into standard Basis-10 numbers. Or, doing things the easy way, add the upper-left numbers in the Groups selected!

NUMERICAL BINGO

This is a game for two.

Each person receives pencil and paper. Players draw a 5-by-5 square of boxes, as shown. Writing done during playing is kept secret until the end.

Take turns calling out any number from 1 through 9. Each person will write the number anywhere, in one of the squares that is empty, one number per square. The winner is the one who has the most rows which add up to 25. There are 12 rows: 5 horizontal, 5 vertical, and the two main diagonals. Scores are counted when all 25 boxes have been filled.

MOVE THE COMPUTERS

The new Computer Manager thought he was a genius. When told that the elevators could not hold the weight of his eight new machines, he hired a huge crane. Leaving instructions to lower the computers through a large skylight in the roof, he then went on his summer vacation.

As soon as he returned, he knew he was in trouble. The moving men had put the computers in the room, but had them in the wrong places. All machines had to be moved. The large drawing shows the way the computers are now positioned. The small drawing is how they should be located.

Cut eight small pieces of paper. Number them 1, 2, 3, 4, 5, 6, 7, 8. Put them on the large drawing, matching the numbers shown. Now, move one machine at a time into a space that is empty, or which later becomes empty. See if you can get the computer room straightened out without hiring the crane again!

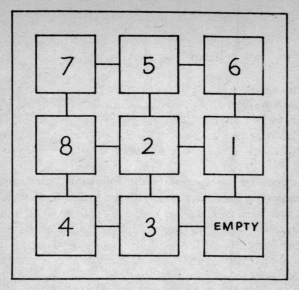

COMPUTERS IN WRONG POSITION

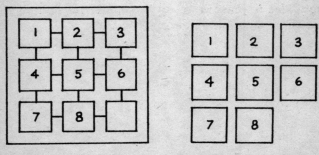

POSITIONS WANTED

Cut and number 8 squares as shown here. Put the pieces on matching numbers in the top drawing.

ANSWER

Move the computers in the following order, into the empty space existing at any time: 1, 2, 3, 1, 2, 6, 5, 3, 1, 2, 6, 5, 3, 1, 2, 4, 8, 7, 1, 2, 4, 8, 7, 4, 5, 6.

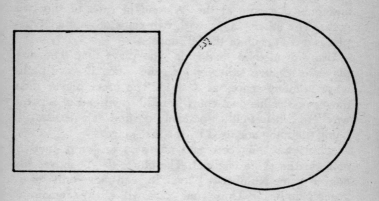

TEST YOUR DEXTERITY

With a pencil in each hand, try drawing a circle and a square. The trick is to draw them at the same time. Do the circle with your left hand, and the square with your right hand.

TWO HEADS ARE BETTER
. . . .SOMETIMES

Two players place coins at opposite ends of the pathways shown. One person has two coins of the same type, and puts one coin at the "A" end of each of the two paths. The other player, with two coins of another type, places one at each of the "B" ends.

Use any method to decide who plays first. The first player can move either of his coins along its own pathway, as many spaces as desired. The other player then moves one of his own coins from his own end of a pathway. He can use either pathway desired, not necessarily being the same one used by the first player.

In playing, one coin can not pass or jump another coin on the same channel. Therefore, if "A" moves his coin to space Number 8, player "B" can move only up to space Number 9. Thus, your coins will always remain at your end of the pathway.

When making a move, either pathway may be used, but only one coin is moved in any single turn. In any play, a coin can be moved as many spaces forward or backward as desired.

The game is won when one player backs the opponent's coins into the starting position, with no further chance for a move.

There is a strategy in playing, but don't look at it until you have tried playing a few games. Then

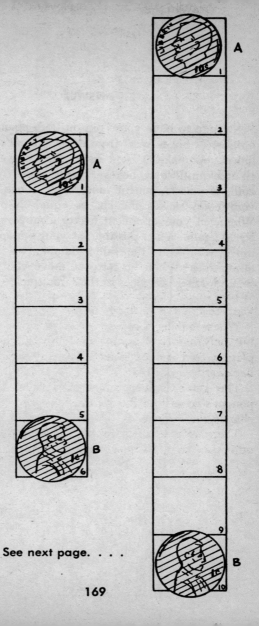

See next page. . . .

ANSWER

Arrange to have your coin on both channels the same number of boxes apart from the opponent's coins in each move you make. If you move first, move on the long channel until four boxes separate you from the other coin. If your opponent moves first, move whichever of your coins makes the spaces equal in both channels. Whenever your opponent makes a move, get the spaces equal again. When possible, as your opponent advances, move your coin the same number of spaces in the other track. When he retreats, move yours forward the same number of spaces in the same track.

THREE-FIVE-TEN

If you like playing word games where knowledge and flexible thinking often pay off well, try this game. It is done with only pencil and paper.

Draw a box of squares, five wide by five deep, as shown. The game is best for two persons.

Each person takes turns naming a letter of the alphabet. It can duplicate another one already used, or can be one unused as yet. Each person places that letter anywhere in the 25 boxes desired. Once there, it can not be erased.

See how many words you have formed, when the game is finished. Each player has placed his letters in any place he wanted, so it is rare that players duplicate their words.

Three-letter words count as three points. Four-letter words are worth five points. Five-letter words score as ten points.

MEMORY TEST

Look at the pictures for 1½ minutes. Then put the book aside. See how many animals you can remember. Ten is good, 12 excellent, and all 14, that's fantastic!

See next page for memory aid. . . .

MEMORY-IMPROVER

If you were able to remember the pictures just by glancing at them, you have a remarkable memory.

If you are like most people, and could not recall all the animals, try making an impromptu story. It helps memorizng a list of items like this. For example, visualize the turtle ambling along, with a butterfly on its back, being passed at high speed by a rabbit which jumps over a pig's back to land near a cricket which hops in fright toward a squirrel. . . .

Relate one picture to the next, inventing any story that comes to your imagination, and which is easy to recall. In such fashion, you have the trick for recalling lists of many unrelated objects.

JUST FOR FUN

Here are a few diversions to try, when you want to try something besides brain-twisting puzzles:

MATCHBOOK: Two people each put a book of paper matches on the back of their right hands. Keep the other hands out of the way. See who can knock off the other's matches, keeping his own intact.

PAPER-DROP: Hold a flat sheet of paper, perhaps letterhead size, by one edge. Allow it to fall. Have your hand at least three to five feet higher than where the other person can try to catch the paper on the way down, using only one finger and thumb. It can be difficult.

BLACK AND BLUE

Here is a game covering the entire continental United States. Two players participate in this contest. Each uses a separate color, such as black and blue, but any two different colors can be used.

Flip a coin to decide who plays first. The beginner marks any state selected, with his own color. The other player then marks any other state, with his own color. Players keep taking turns coloring states, but a player may not use his color on a state which touches or borders on a state he has previously colored with his own color.

For example, if Utah is colored by a player, then he can not fill in Idaho, Nevada, Arizona, Wyoming or Colorado. The corner-to-corner state of New Mexico would be acceptable, however.

The winner is the last player to color a state, leaving no available state for the other person to color, according to the game rules.

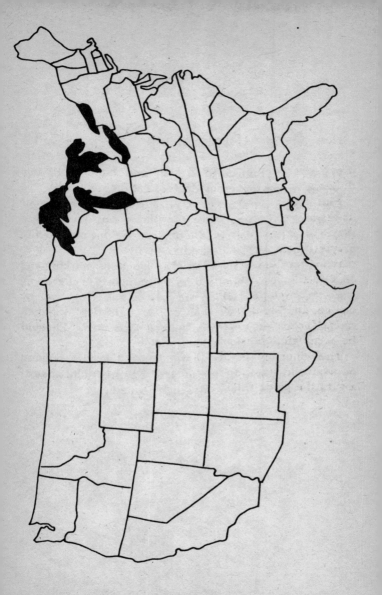

YOUR TURN!

Try to get from A to Z first, and hope that your opponent makes the wrong decisions at the right time!

The first player starts with A, putting a circle around it. Since in the same move the player can mark either one, two or three letters, a circle can be put around the B and even the C, if desired.

The other player then has the chance of marking the next one, two or three letters in sequence, using an X over them, to show which are his.

Keep alternating as you go through the alphabet, marking one, two or three letters each turn. Whoever lands on Z first is the winner.

Each column is a separate game. The last column shown, by the way, is the ancient Egyptian alphabet of 24 characters, with two extra signs added.

A	1	I	𓅃
B	2	II	𓃀
C	3	III	𓏥
D	4	IV	𓂧
E	5	V	𓅂
F	6	VI	𓆑
G	7	VII	𓊪
H	8	VIII	𓂋
I	9	IX	𓅀
J	10	X	𓈖
K	11	XI	𓏤
L	12	XII	𓊗
M	13	XIII	�
N	14	XIV	𓇳
O	15	XV	𓌟
P	16	XVI	𓏏
Q	17	XVII	𓊃
R	18	XVIII	𓎛
S	19	XIX	𓎼
T	20	XX	𓎿
U	21	XXI	𓏌
V	22	XXII	𓎡
W	23	XXIII	𓐍
X	24	XXIV	𓆓
Y	25	XXV	𓋴
Z	26	XXVI	𓎬

PUZZLE THAT GROWS

Here is a collection of letters which is as well mixed as the soil in a freshly spaded garden plot. Sprinkle a handful of miscellaneous seeds on the ground, and you may be amazed at what you can find there after a while.

With enough patience and nurturing of your alphabetic garden, you may find the following items. You'll probably see some other items of plant life too, when you examine the plot carefully. Encircle all plants as you find them.

Names are given in a straight line. However, those names may be downward, upward, vertical, horizontal, diagonal, forward or backward. Occasionally the same letters are used for more than one word. We'll start you off with BUSH.

acacia	geranium	pine
anemone	grass	plants
arbutus	goldenrod	pod
aster	heather	poinsettia
azalea	herbs	poppy
bud	honeysuckle	posy
bush	iris	reed
cactus	ivy	rhododendron
camellia	lilac	root
carnation	lily	rose
chrysanthemum	lotus	rosemary
cotton	marigold	sage
crocus	moss	shrub
dahlia	oleander	stock
daisy	orchid	trees
fern	pansy	vines
flax	peony	weeds
gardenia	phlox	

	A	B	C	D	E	F	G	H	I	J	K	L	M	N	O
1	C	A	M	E	L	L	I	A	E	N	O	M	E	N	A
2	A	H	A	D	O	I	C	R	O	S	E	M	A	R	Y
3	R	O	R	E	T	L	G	B	I	B	A	S	S	O	M
4	N	N	I	Y	U	A	E	U	G	S	I	G	T	F	G
5	A	E	G	P	S	C	R	T	R	U	C	F	E	R	N
6	T	Y	O	P	H	A	A	U	A	C	A	B	R	O	P
7	I	S	L	O	R	C	N	S	S	O	C	U	R	D	A
8	O	U	D	P	U	T	I	T	S	R	A	D	S	O	N
9	N	C	C	I	B	U	U	B	H	C	N	E	T	R	S
10	H	K	O	P	T	S	M	H	U	E	P	E	O	N	Y
11	E	L	T	L	R	W	E	E	D	S	M	R	C	E	G
12	R	E	T	A	E	R	O	O	T	J	H	U	K	D	A
13	B	D	O	N	E	A	D	A	H	L	I	A	M	L	R
14	S	I	N	T	S	O	N	A	Z	A	L	E	A	O	D
15	F	H	Y	S	H	P	O	D	I	P	I	N	E	G	E
16	L	C	L	R	W	V	I	N	E	S	D	Y	V	I	N
17	A	R	I	H	E	A	T	H	E	R	Y	S	O	P	I
18	X	O	L	H	P	O	I	N	S	E	T	T	I	A	A

Turn page, for solution to the plant locations. . . .

ANSWERS

The numbers and letters after each name show the location of the first and second letters of the word in the puzzle:

acacia—8K, 7K
anemone—1O, 1N
arbutus—1H, 2H
aster—2M, 3M
azalea—14H, 14I
bud—6L, 7N
bush—9H, 10I
cactus—5F, 6F
camellia—1A, 1B
carnation—1A, 2A
chrysanthemum—1C, 2B
cotton—9D, 10D
crocus—9J, 8J
dahlia—13G, 13H
daisy—13G, 14H
fern—5L, 5M
flax—15A, 16A
gardenia—11O, 12O
geranium—3G, 4G
grass—4I, 5I
goldenrod—15N, 14N
heather—17D, 17E
herbs—10A, 11A
honeysuckle—2B, 3B
iris—1G, 2H
ivy—16N, 16M

lilac—1F, 2F
lily—18C, 17C
lotus—1E, 2E
marigold—1C, 2C
moss—3O, 3N
oleander—10C, 11D
orchid—18B, 17B
pansy—6O, 7O
peony—10K, 10L
phlox—18E, 18D
pine—15J, 15K
plants—10D, 11D
pod—15F, 15G
poinsettia—18E, 18F
poppy—8D, 7D
posy—17N, 17M
reed—11L, 10L
rhododendron—16D, 15E
root—12F, 12G
rose—2H, 2I
sage—2J, 3K
shrub—5E, 6E
stock—8M, 9M
trees—10E, 11E
vines—16F, 16G
weeds—11F, 11G

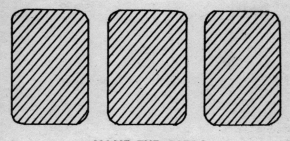

NAME THE CARDS

From a deck of cards, three cards have been removed and placed face-down. There are two Jacks and a Ten. Can you tell the suit and number of each of the three cards, and also indicate which card is which, in the illustration?

Here are some hints:

1. There are two Jacks, both next to each other.
2. There is a 10 next to one of the Jacks.
3. Two Clubs are next to each other.
4. A heart is to the right of a Club.

If you're stuck, turn page for the answer. . . .

ANSWER

10 of Clubs, Jack of Clubs, Jack of Hearts

A	B	C	D
E	F	G	H
I	J	K	L
M	N	O	P

MAGIC-MAGIC SQUARE

Write the number 1 through 16, without skipping or duplicating any figures. Apply one number to each of the 16 boxes. Do so in such a way that each horizontal row totals 34, each vertical row is 34, and the two main diagonals equal 34.

At the same time, the numbers, if properly placed, can have the figures at boxes ADMP add up to 34. Also, the following alphabetic groups can simultaneously equal 34: FGJK, BCNO, EIHL, CENL, and BIOH.

If you solve this square, you can consider yourself having done a good hard day's work!

Turn the page, if you seek the solution.

ANSWER

16	3	2	13
5	10	11	8
9	6	7	12
4	15	14	1

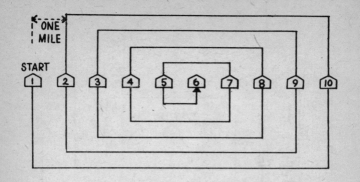

MORE MILEAGE POSSIBLE

Sam did well selling by telephone and chatting pleasantly with his customers. But this irked the new Sales Manager, who felt salesmen ought to be on the road visiting customers personally. So Sam went out, as instructed. His customers were one mile apart along the highway, which, counting the nine miles between them, would give him a quick trip.

But Sam followed the company rules that allowed him to visit each customer just once, and be paid 20-cents a mile. Cleverly, he devised the route shown here, which is 45 miles long, without duplicating visits. As shown, he drove from customer Number 1 to Number 10, then to 2, and so forth.

With a little more thought, the trip could have been made without duplicating visits, yet earn even more mileage. See if you can figure it out, counting miles from the first customer visited.

Turn the page, to see how it can be done. . . .

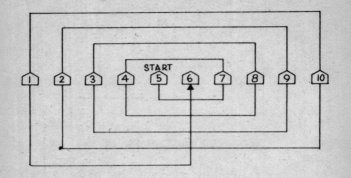

ANSWER

Sam could have added four more miles to his expense voucher, if he would have driven the route shown here, starting with Store Number 5. This would give him a total of 49 miles.

OBSERVATION SKILLS

In the mathematics class, the teacher wanted to see how observant his students were. He drew a small box as shown, connected the corners, and put a dot at the intersection. "Now," he said, "visualize each box in the larger drawing with a dot at the intersections of the 87 boxes. Any dots that could be connected by lines which would form a perfect square should be counted. For example, three squares are: 77-78-67-66-77; 66-78-68-56-66; 55-79-59-36-55. Counting all possible squares in the drawing, when the dots are connected, how many do you see?"

Try it. Then turn page for the answer. . . .

ANSWER

There is a total of 575 squares, actually!

Squares	Typical size, angle, and location
66	77—78—67—66—77
48	77—79—57—55—77
32	77—80—47—44—77
19	78—82—39—35—78
10	78—83—31—26—78
4	78—84—23—17—78
57	79—69—57—67—79
33	47—30—11—26—47
15	80—50—19—44—80
3	82—43— 7—35—82
82	79—58—45—66—79
56	80—48—35—66—80
42	80—49—27—55—80
32	82—40—27—67—82
24	83—42—20—57—83
14	82—42—12—45—14
16	82—31—17—66—82
10	82—32—10—55—82
6	82—33— 5—44—82
4	84—24—10—67—84
2	84—25— 5—56—84

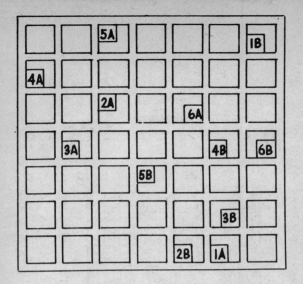

AVOID THY NEIGHBOR

A surprising discovery has just been made that six people in beautiful Havencrest Gardens housing development go for a walk at the same time each day to visit someone in the same area. Yet the strollers never encounter each other, and never cross the same path. A fence around the area limits their walks. And oddly enough, every corner is visited by one of the walkers. None pass on opposite sides of the street.

Number 1A visits 1B, 2A visits 2B, and so forth through 6A going to 6B. Can you draw the route taken by each person? Paths start at the street corner on which each house is located.

For the routes taken, turn the page. . . .

ANSWER

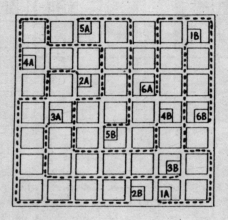